INTRODUCTI⟨

G000166516

Over the years road locomotives have performed many herculean feat⟨
and difficult loads over long distances. Probably the best known engines on t⟨
by Norman Box; other road locomotives were responsible for the haulage of ⟨
from the works to the docks. Many engines were used on haulage duties ⟨... much more⟩ localized area.

Fortunately a considerable number of these magnificent and powerful engines have survived into preservation, and can even be seen on occasions demonstrating heavy haulage. Naturally, the sight of two or three engines working hard attracts considerable attention. Often it is extremely difficult to obtain a satisfactory photograph for a number of reasons. Ooccasionally the conditions are right and a worthwhile shot is obtained such as the picture which is to be found at the head of the Preface page, taken when these road engines were in 'full cry', providing never to be forgotten sights and sounds as they tackled a hilly section in Dorset.

The majority of road locomotives in preservation are engines built by Fowlers of Leeds whose B5 and B6 'Super Lion' designs were extremely popular with heavy haulage contractors. Examples of other Fowler designs also exist. In addition a considerable number of Burrell road locomotives are to be seen on the rally fields, with 'Lord Roberts', 'Conqueror' and 'Duke of Kent' being superb examples.

Several other engine builders have a few survivors, among these is the sole Garrett road locomotive 'Vera', which spent its working life in Northern Ireland. McLarens of Leeds are represented by four engines, together with the same number built by Aveling & Porter.

As with the other Steam Albums, the contents include engines which are rarely seen in public and also those which attend events in many parts of the country. The photographs within this album, the fifth in the series, complete one more section of engine types, which when the series is complete will provide a very representative selection of the types of engines which have survived into preservation. A fitting tribute to British engineering!

Left: The Burrell crane engine no. 4074 built in 1927 does not attend many rallies. The forecarriage and wheels of this engine are extra strong to accommodate the crane and can be clearly seen. The engine has been named after the River Lark. Burrells built a total of 32 crane engines from 1886 onwards.

1. *Very few road locomotives built by Aveling & Porter have survived into preservation, this one is works number 8471 built in 1914, being a three speed 6NHP compound design. When new the engine was supplied for general haulage work to an owner in Farnham, Surrey, since then the engine has had several owners including at one time being part of the Alton Towers collection.*

2. *Another view of Aveling 8471 taken in 1988, showing the flywheel side, note the engine was on straked wheels at this time, having collected a fair amount of mud when this photograph was taken.*

3. 'Emperor' was originally built as a showmans locomotive for C. Twigden of Lutterworth in 1895. In 1906 the engine returned to Burrells when the crane was added, becoming their yard engine. This 10NHP 2 speed engine works no. 1876 has now been restored to showmans condition.

4. The ex. Burrell works engine 'Emperor' seen here at Raynham, Norfolk in 1962, the engine was fitted with crane no. 1222. At one time the engine was part of the Holywell (Cambs) collection and was sold at the engine sale in October 1980.

5. Burrell 'The President' no. 2789 of 1905 is part of the famous Bressingham collection. The engine is a 8NHP double crank three speed compound weighing 16 tons and having a top speed of 10mph.

6. 'The President', this superb Burrell road locomotive no. 2789 began its works life as a showmans road locomotive for President Kemp of Leicester, but after a few years was converted to a road engine. The engine is seen here at an early 1960s rally.

7. *Burrell 7NHP compound 3 speed road locomotive no. 2646 was built at Thetford in 1904, which makes it one of the oldest surviving road engines built by this well respected engine builder, and unusual in being a single crank compound.*

8. *'Lord Roberts', a superb example of the Burrell 'contractors engine', being of heavier construction than usual. The 7NHP 3 speed engine was built at Thetford in 1908 as works number 3057. During its working life this engine was responsible for haulage of timber, bricks and boilers, ending up lying derelict for over 15 years before being restored for preservation.*

9. In 1911 'Clinker' was supplied new to the Wingham Agricultural Co. Ltd. who used the engine on haulage work, until a few years later when it was passed into the ownership of a company in Sussex. Among the engines last work was dredging in the Fens of East Anglia. 'Clinker' was built at Thetford as works number 3257, being a 7NHP 3 speed double crank compound design.

10. This fine Burrell 6NHP 3 speed road engine 'The Dalesman' was built at Thetford in 1911 as works number 3395, when new the engine was supplied to Hancocks Brickworks, Exeter, later passing into the ownership of Hentons of Hopwas, Staffordshire and used for haulage in the potteries.

11. 'Dreadnought' as it was in 1961. This Burrell engine is works number 3118 and was built at the 'St. Nicholas Works' in 1909 as a showmans engine, being supplied new to Wm. Cross, Workington. Note the straked wheels which the youthful admirer is pointing at.

12. A much travelled Burrell road locomotive which regularly take part in 'Amalgamated Heavy Haulage' demonstrations is 'Duke of Kent', this fine Burrell 6NHP 3 speed engine, works number 3593 was built at Thetford in 1914. The Burrells first owners were C. Tassell of Chatham, Kent who used the engine for general haulage work, five years later the engine was sold to Scotts Sawmills, also of Chatham, where it performed a dual role of driving machinery during the day, and haulage of finished timber during the night, the engine passed through several other owners until becoming disused in the early fifties.

13. For a number of years Burrell 3593 'Duke of Kent' was to be seen without a canopy, this photograph shows the engine in 1981 and reveals many details on this fine road locomotive. Extra water capacity in the form of 'belly' tanks, and sprung front and rear axles were normal on most road locomotives.

14. Another interesting photograph taken in the early sixties, this time of 'His Majesty'. a 6NHP Burrell crane engine no. 3829 built in 1920 and supplied new to owners in Liskeard, Cornwall, after only a matter of months the engine was purchased by Messrs. J Hickey & Sons Ltd. who used the engine for heavy haulage work in the London area.

15. 'Lord Fisher of Lambeth' photographed in 1972, Burrells of Thetford built this 6NHP road locomotive in 1919 as works number 3824, unlike many other road locomotives this particular engine was supplied in showmans colours to its new owner near Taunton, Somerset, who used the engine for timber work and other agricultural duties. Prior to delivery the engine was exhibited at the Royal Dairy show in London.

16. Several fine road engines are in preservation in the county of Cornwall including the 6NHP Burrell 'Janet', which was built at Thetford in 1922 as works number 3937. This engine spent its entire working life in Scotland, going new to an owner in Crathes, Kincardinshire, having first been exhibited at the 'Highland Show'. During its working life, it worked on the Balmoral estate and also at Peterculter.

17. Two Burrell road locomotives caught by the camera in the early part of the day, on the left is 5NHP number 3996 'Conqueror' built in 1924, the other engine built five years earlier is the 6NHP 'Lord Fisher of Lambeth'. An interesting photograph enabling one to compare the 5 & 6NHP designs.

18. Another of the Burrell road locomotives preserved in Cornwall is 'Conqueror' which was built in 1924 as works number 3996, going new to J H Henton of Tamworth, like so many engines it ended its working life on threshing work. The engine is a 5NHP 3 speed design.

19. 'The Lark', a splendid example of a Burrell crane engine was supplied new to a Bury St. Edmunds timber company in 1927. This engine is works number 4074 and is a 3 speed engine of 5NHP. This particular crane engine was the last built by the company.

20. When purchased this 7NHP Foden road locomotive was in a derelict condition, many hours of careful restoration have resulted in the magnificently restored engine which is seen today. This engine is number 1294, and was built at Sandbach in 1909.

21. *Foden 8NHP 'Colonial' type road locomotive number 3534 was built in 1913 and supplied new to the Earl of Derby, who used the engine for forestry work. Only five of this type of engine were built, the other four being shipped overseas. Note the extra long firebox designed for burning wood or straw.*

22. *The flywheel side of 'Monarch', this engine has Foden's high pressure system with patented double high valve. This fine road locomotive does not attend many rallies.*

23. *Foden of Sandbach, Cheshire built this 6NHP 3 speed road locomotive in 1914 as works number 4752, it was supplied new to Barland of Kilmarnock for agricultural duties, in 1920 it passed into the ownership of the showman Cadona Bros. who used the engine for haulage, this fine engine ended its days, like so many more, on threshing work. In preservation it was converted to a showmans, and in 1988 it was converted back to a road locomotive at the 'Great Dorset Steam Fair'. 'Sandy Macnab' is thought to be the only 6NHP Foden road locomotive surviving in this country. Note the side damper flap to the ashpan, a feature of the Foden design.*

24. *'Lord Roberts', and 'Wolverhampton Wanderer' photographed starting away with a heavy load of timber. 'Lord Roberts' is Burrell 3057 of 1908 the Fowler is number 17212 built at Leeds in 1929.*

25. *Another heavy haulage demonstration gets under way at Knebworth with Burrell 3593 'Duke of Kent' as lead engine, followed by two Fowler B6 class engines 'Wolverhampton Wanderer' and 'Atlas'.*

26. *One of the oldest Fowler road locomotives in existence is number 8712 'Prince of Wales' which was built in 1900. When new the engine was supplied to J H & R O Morse, Haulage Contractors of Narbeth in Pembrokeshire, by the thirties the engine was driving machinery at a quarry, later reverting to its original haulage work. The engine is a 6NHP A4 class compound.*

27. *Another photograph of no. 8712 'Prince of Wales', this time showing clearly the front end of this interesting Fowler road locomotive. This engine is often to be seen at the 'Great Dorset Steam Fair'.*

28. *This fine B5 class Fowler road locomotive was supplied new in 1900 to a brickworks at Market Lavington. 'Lord Roberts' is a 7NHP 3 speed double crank compound engine. Note the extra 'belly tanks' for additional water supplies on long journeys. The works number of this engine is 8903, for a number of years it was part of the Holywell (Cambs) collection, and was sold with the other engines in 1980.*

29. 'Princess' pictured here with a considerable amount of Dorset mud on its wheels. This D2 class 5NHP Fowler road locomotive was built at Leeds in 1910 and carries. works number 12255. When new the engine was used on haulage duties being converted a few years later to full showmans specification by Richard Townsend & Sons of Weymouth Dorset and used on showland duties until the last war, when it was employed on haulage and agricultural duties.

30. For comparison another much earlier photograph of 'Princess' taken in 1972 showing the engine still carrying a dynamo bracket, also visible are several other smaller changes in the appearance of this smart Fowler 5NHP engine.

Plate 1.   Fowler D2 class road locomotive no. 12899 'Western Star'. This 5NHP engine was built at the Leeds works in 1912, and supplied new to Carmarthen County Council for stone hauling. In 1922 it passed into the ownership of a Contractor who used it for threshing and driving a saw mill.

Plate 2. Burrell 7NHP road locomotive 'Lord Roberts' was built at Thetford in 1908 as works number 3057, being a contractors engine it is more heavily contructed than usual. The engine was supplied new to Wm. Smith of North Warnborough and used on haulage of building materials. In 1919 the engine was sold to a new owner in Lincolnshire where it remained in use until 1940.

Plate 3. McLaren 1332 'Gigantic' spent most of its working life in Australia. This fine 10NHP compound road locomotive has been completely rebuilt over the last few years and is now frequently seen on the rally fields.

Plate 4.. 'Boadicea' has been a familiar engine on the rally fields for many years. Over fifty of these 10NHP McLarens were built for the War Department for gun haulage, this one, built in 1919, being completed after the war was over. Number 1652 was sold to a private owner and used on haulage work, at one stage it was owned by Edwin Corrigan and used on showland work, the engine was found to be too heavy and passed into the ownership of Shaw & Gaskell of Hull where it was also used for heavy haulage. As with so many engines it ended its days on agricultural work.

Plate 5. Majestic road locomotives built by Fowler & Burrell stand side by side. The Fowler is the B6 class no. 17212 'Wolverhampton Wanderer' with the Burrell 3593 'Duke of Kent' alongside, both engines are familiar with a great many people, as both travel extensively, including on the continent.

Plate 6. One very well known road locomotive is the 6NHP Burrell no. 3593 'Duke of Kent', which was built in 1914. The engine was supplied new to Mr. Tassell of Chatham, a few years later it passed into the ownership of Scots Sawmills, also at Chatham, regularly working to London with timber, the engine had several other owners before being purchased for preservation.

Plate 7. *Burrell 6NHP road locomotive 'Lord Fisher of Lambeth', a fine example of the three speed double crank compound design. This engine was built in 1919 as works number 3824, being exhibited at the Royal Dairy show and going to an owner at Taunton Somerset with who it remained for its entire working life.*

Plate 8. *Fowler D5 class 19338 'Monty' was built in 1931. This 5NHP road locomotive was supplied new to Englefields Estate in Berkshire and looks in this photograph, very much as it would have done during its working days.*

31. *Fowler B6 class road locomotive number 12226 'Titan' was built at Leeds in 1911. Note the wooden tyres fitted to the engine.*

32. *Several examples of the Fowler D2 class road locomotive are in preservation, this one is preserved in Cornwall. This 5NHP engine is works number 12693 'Brunel', built in 1911 and was photographed in 1968.*

33. 'Western Star' commenced its working life hauling stone for its owners Carmarthen County Council to whom it was supplied new in 1912. In 1922 this engine changed hands, when it was primarily used on agricultural duties ending its working days during the first part of the last war driving a saw bench. This D2 class Fowler is works number 12899, being a 5NHP engine.

34. Fowler 5NHP D2 class road locomotive 'Activity' photographed here with a Fowler traction wagon built in 1920. This engine was built at Leeds in 1913 as works number 12902 and supplied new to a Kent market gardener travelling frequently to the London Covent Garden market. After changing hands this engine was familiar in Worcestershire and Gloucestershire on general haulage work.

35. *Several classes of Fowler road locomotives are in preservation, this one, 'Finella' is a fine example of the A7 class, built at Leeds in 1914 as works number 13138. When new the engine was supplied to an owner in Auchinblae, Kincardineshire, the same county in which it is now preserved.*

36. *Another view of 'Finella', this time showing the flywheel side of the engine, which is a 7NHP 3 speed design. Among the last duties of this fine Fowler was timber extraction.*

37. *Fowler road locomotive 14888 is an example of the 7NHP R3 class, originally built in 1917 for the War Department for the Russian Front, but due to various circumstances it was sold on the home market to a Hampshire contractor, the engine was later sold to a Northamptonshire owner and in due course was purchased by Tom Burton Haulage Contractors of Market Harborough.*

38. *Fowler class 7NHP A9 road locomotive number 15462 'Belle of the Wolds' was supplied to H. Packer of Cheltenham when new in 1919, as with so many road engines ending its working days on agricultural duties.*

39. 'Endeavour' is a 7NHP Fowler number 14754 an A8 class design built at this Leeds works in 1920, being supplied new to Drage & Kent in Suffolk who used the engine on general haulage work.

40. Another photograph from the rally archives, this time showing the Fowler road engine, number 14754 'Endeavour' being polished at Ickleton in 1962. The engine was fitted with a different canopy at this time.

41. This photograph also from early rally days archives shows the Fowler road locomotive number 15323 'Excelsior' as it was in 1963. This A9 class road locomotive was built in 1918.

42. 'Excelsior' is an excellent example of the A9 class of Fowler road locomotive, the engine was constructed for the War Department in 1918 as Fowler, works number 15323, two years later it was sold to Samuel Jackson & Son, Haulage Contractors of Crewe, remaining in their ownership and used until 1946 when it passed into the ownership of a Derbyshire farmer and was used for threshing work.

43. Another early sixties picture taken at Rempstone of the Fowler 'Excelsior' this time showing the flywheel side of the engine. Considerable changes have been made to this engine since this photograph was taken.

44. A quiet moment for two Fowler road locomotives seen here standing side by side, on the left is number 8712, an A4 class built in 1900 and named 'Prince of Wales', the crane engine is B6 class number 17106 'Duke of York'.

45. *Norman E Box of Manchester operated a number of Fowler road locomotives, 'Atlas', number 17105 is the sole survivor. This B6 class engine and the others were responsible for hauling massive loads throughout the United Kingdom.*

46. *'Titan' and 'Atlas' pause for a moment before commencing a downhill section during a road run in Herefordshire. Both of these fine Fowlers are B6 class engines.*

47. *'Duke of York' is a superb example of the Fowler B6 class, this engine was built in 1928 as works number 17106, during its working life for Marstons Road Services, Liverpool it was responsible for haulage of many heavy items including transformers, castings, dynamos, and in 1939 the engine hauled the rudder of 'HMS Ark Royal' from Darlington to Birkenhead.*

48. *Fowler 10NHP road locomotive number 17106 'Duke of York' prepares to assist with a heavy haulage demonstration, this B6 class engine spent most of its working life with Marstons Road Services, Liverpool. Details of the jib crane can be clearly seen in this photograph.*

49. The widely known Fowler B6 'Super Lion' 'Wolverhampton Wanderer' has attended many rallies in this country, and also on the continent. This Fowler was supplied new to John Thompson of Ettingshall, Wolverhampton in 1929, and used to deliver 'Lancashire' type boilers over a wide area, after 1948 the engine was used as a crane engine in the stock yard. The engine is works number 17212, a 8NHP engine weighing in at 21 tons.

50. This view of 'Wolverhampton Wanderer' shows the engine without the crane fitted, considerably altering its appearance. As can be seen this engine was taking part in a heavy haulage demonstration when this photograph was taken.

51. *This interesting and unusual photograph shows three Fowler B6 class road engines at the head of a heavy load, during a haulage demonstration at Knebworth in 1986. The engines are 'Duke of York', 'Wolverhampton Wanderer' (without crane) and 'Atlas'.*

52. *Another photograph of 'Wolverhampton Wanderer', this time taken from the rear and showing the flywheel side of this massive engine as it prepares to join in another heavy haulage demonstration.*

53. *Fowlers and Burrells were the two major builders of road locomotives. The massive crane engine 'Wolverhampton Wanderer' and Burrell number 3996 'Conqueror' stand ready at the start of the day.*

54. *This Garrett road locomotive 'Vera' is one of the small number of engines, apart from rollers, which passed straight from its owners into preservation. 'Vera' is the only surviving Garrett road locomotive and was built at Leiston in 1909 as works number 27946, being a 6NHP two speed engine. The engine was supplied new to J Harkness of Belfast for whom it worked until 1967.*

55. This much travelled McLaren road locomotive spent its working life in Australia, returning home in the early 1980's, now fully rebuilt it proudly carries the name 'Gigantic', a particularly apt name for this large 10NHp engine which was built in 1912 as works number 1322.

56. 'Captain Scott' is a McLaren 8NHP road locomotive, works number 1421 built at Leeds in 1913. Only four McLaren road locomotives survive in preservation in the United Kingdom.

57. *Road locomotives built by two principal engine builders stand side by side, on the left is the McLaren 8NHP number 1421, a 3 speed compound named 'Captain Scott', the other engine is the Fowler 'Excelsior', a 7NHP class A9 number 15323, built in 1918.*

58. *This photograph is one of my earliest traction engine pictures, it shows McLaren 1652 'Boadicea' on its way home to Saffron Walden in 1960. Note the engine was on straked wheels at that time. The photograph was taken in Huntingdon, nothing remains now of any of the buildings in the background.*

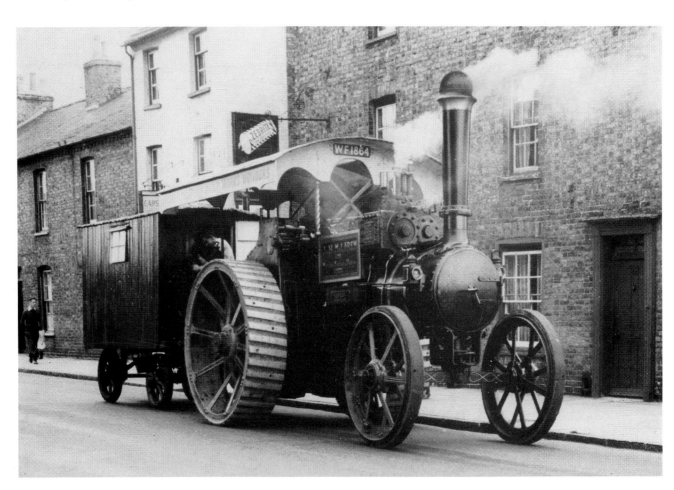

59. *McLarens of Leeds built a considerable number of road engines for the War Department, included among them was this one 'Boadicea', number 1652 built in 1919. After the end of hostilities many were purchased for haulage work as happened with 'Boadicea', in this case it was later to be converted to full showmans specification for Edwin Corrigan of Filey, Yorkshire, due to the engine being found to heavy for this work it was sold again for haulage work.*

60. *An early rally photograph of 'Boadicea' when it attended the Chatteris rally in July 1963, at the time it was owned by Mr. Steve Neville and regularly attended rallies under its own steam. several changes can be seen on the more recent photograph.*

61. *Front end detail of Fowler A9 class no. 15323 'Excelsior' can be clearly seen in this photograph, as it stands in the sunshine at the 'Great Dorset Steam Fair', an ideal event to see these fine locomotives put through their paces.*